Leo learns Cricket

From the series "Leo Learns"
Written by Simon Lambert

Illustrations by Dave Collins

Toddler Sports Limited

"Sowing the seeds of sport for a healthier childhood."

First published in Great Britain 2007
by Toddler Sports Limited - U.K. England

"Leo Learns Cricket" written by Simon Lambert
© Toddler Sports Limited

Illustrations by Dave Collins
© Dave Collins

"Leo Learns" and "Laura Learns"
© Toddler Sports Limited

ISBN 978-1-905947-02-7

Printed in China

Leo loves to play sport; it keeps him active and healthy.

It also helps him make lots of new friends.

One day Leo wanted to learn how to play the game of cricket.

He decided to find someone who could teach him, so he went to the place where it is played:

The cricket club!

At the club Leo met Mr Googly the cricket coach.

"Hello Mr Googly," said Leo. "I would like to learn about cricket. Can you help me?"

"Yes I can," replied Mr Googly. "My job is to teach people how to play cricket - would you like me to teach you?"

"Yes please!" said Leo with a big smile.

Mr Googly showed Leo a big blue cricket bag.

"All you need to start playing cricket is in this bag," said Mr Googly.

"There are some red cricket balls, a pair of white gloves, some leg pads, a helmet and a cricket bat. There are also some stumps and bails."

"What are they all for?" asked Leo.

"Let me explain," said Mr Googly.

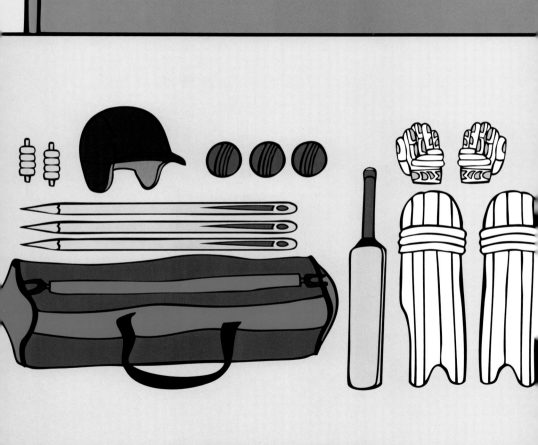

"The cricket bat is used to hit the ball," said Mr Googly, and he gave Leo a red cricket ball.

"This is a hard ball," said Leo.

"Because the ball is hard you should wear gloves to protect your hands, pads to protect your legs and a helmet to protect your head," explained Mr Googly.

"Finally these three stumps are pushed together into the ground and the two small bails are placed on top, like this."

Mr Googly and Leo went to watch a game of cricket being played at the club.

"The white outline around the field is called the boundary and it marks the playing area," said Mr Googly. "Do you see the rectangle in the middle of the field?" he asked.

"Yes," replied Leo.

"That is called the wicket. It has three stumps and two bails at each end," explained Mr Googly.

They found some seats and sat down ready to watch the game.

Leo noticed that there were lots of people on the cricket field.

"Who are all the people on the field?" asked Leo.

"The two people holding bats are called batsmen," replied Mr Googly. "The man holding the ball is the bowler, and the people all around are called the fielders."

"Who is the person in the long white jacket wearing a hat?" asked Leo.

"That is the umpire, and he is in charge of the match," replied Mr Googly.

"Cricket is played between two teams. The batting team scores points by hitting the ball around the field," explained Mr Googly. "The other team must try to stop the batsmen scoring by getting them out. It is called the fielding team."

"How does the fielding team get a batsman out?" asked Leo.

"A batsman can be out if he hits the ball in the air and it is caught. He can also be out if the ball hits the stumps," explained Mr Googly. "Once the fielding team gets ten batsmen out, it is their turn to bat."

Leo noticed another person standing behind the stumps. "Who is that person wearing big red gloves?" he asked.

"That is the wicketkeeper, and he is there to stop the ball if it goes behind the stumps," replied Mr Googly.

"Do you know how many players there are in a cricket team, Leo?" he asked.

Leo began to count the players on the fielding team.

"One, two, three, four, five, six, seven, eight, nine, ten... eleven?" asked Leo.

"Well done, Leo. That is correct - there are eleven players in a cricket team," said Mr Googly.

Mr Googly pointed to a large black and white board in the distance.

"That is the scoreboard and it shows how many points have been scored," he explained. "Points in cricket are called runs and the team with the most runs wins the game."

"How do you score runs?" asked Leo.

"The batsman scores a run by running to the other end of the wicket once he hits the ball. Runs can also be scored by hitting the ball over the boundary," replied Mr Googly.

The umpire stood with his arm raised – the match was about to begin...

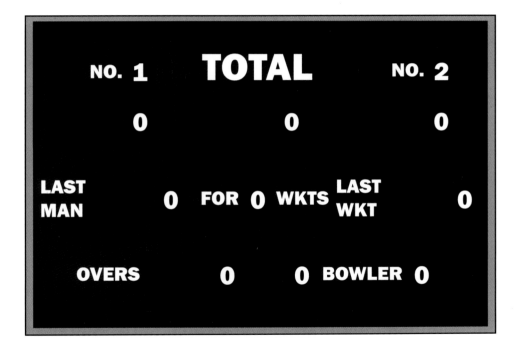

The umpire brought his arm down to his side and called, "Play!"

"Now the bowler can start the game," said Mr Googly.

The bowler ran towards the wicket and bowled the ball quickly at the stumps – *Whoosh!*

The batsman swung his bat, hitting the ball along the ground, and ran to the other end of the wicket.

"Has that batsman just scored one run?" asked Leo?

"Yes, he has. Well done Leo," said Mr Googly.

Leo enjoyed watching how the batsmen hit different shots around the field to score runs.

Suddenly one batsman hit a shot very hard – *Crack!* The ball flew high in the air and bounced over the boundary.

"Wow, what a great shot!" said Leo.

"That shot is called a six and scores six runs," explained Mr Googly.

The batsman then hit another good shot. This time the ball ran along the ground and bounced over the boundary.

"That shot is called a four and scores four runs," Mr Googly added.

Leo thought that hitting those shots looked like fun.

The bowler started to bowl his next ball. He ran towards the wicket and flung the ball very quickly towards the batsman – *Whoosh!*

The ball flew towards the batsman who swung his bat but the ball was going too fast.

Clunk! The ball hit the stumps and the bails flew into the air!

"Hooray!" cheered the fielding team.

"Is that batsman out?" asked Leo.

"Yes, he is," replied Mr Googly.

When the game had finished Mr Googly asked, "Would you like to come and practise with me, Leo?"

"Yes please," replied Leo excitedly.

Mr Googly gave Leo some cricket equipment. Leo put pads on his legs, gloves on his hands and a helmet on his head to protect him.

"I am ready now," said Leo.

"Do you see the line just in front of the stumps Leo?" asked Mr Googly.

"Yes," replied Leo.

"That is called the crease. You must stand with at least one leg between that line and the stumps," explained Mr Googly.

Mr Googly bowled the ball slowly to Leo.

Leo moved towards the ball and swung his bat quickly, but he missed the ball completely.

"Don't worry," said Mr Googly. "Try to watch the ball carefully and swing your bat smoothly," he suggested.

Mr Googly bowled another ball to Leo. This time Leo kept his eyes on the ball and swung his bat - *Thud!* He hit the ball.

"Well done, Leo. That is much better," said Mr Googly.

As he hit more shots, Leo concentrated on the ball. Soon he was hitting it well.

"Now I will show you how to bowl the ball, Leo," said Mr Googly.

"When you bowl, your foot must not land past the crease at this end of the wicket," he said.

Leo took off his pads, gloves and helmet and picked up the ball.

"Try and bowl it underarm first and see if you can hit the stumps," said Mr Googly.

Leo threw the ball underarm down the wicket and hit the stumps first time!

"Very good, Leo," said Mr Googly.

"Now you can try bowling overarm," he said.

Bowling overarm meant that Leo had to swing his arm quickly over his head to bowl the ball. It was more difficult than bowling underarm, and Leo found it hard to hit the stumps.

"Don't worry, Leo. Bowling overarm takes a bit more practice," said Mr Googly.

"Looks like I will be here for a while!" joked Leo.

"Ha! Ha!" laughed Mr Googly.

Leo was really enjoying cricket with Mr Googly.

"There is one more thing I would like you to try, Leo," said Mr Googly. "When I throw the ball, I want you to catch it before it hits the ground."

Mr Googly threw the ball up in the air. Leo held out one hand to try and catch the ball, but he dropped it.

"Let's try again," said Mr Googly. "This time cup both of your hands together."

Mr Googly threw the ball in the air again. This time Leo managed to catch the ball using both hands; he was very pleased.

"Well done, Leo! You have learnt the basics of cricket," said Mr Googly. "You can practise at home with your friends. All you need is a bat, some stumps and a soft ball like a tennis ball."

"Why a soft ball?" asked Leo.

"It is better to use a soft ball as you won't need a helmet or pads to protect you," replied Mr Googly.

Leo couldn't wait to get home and show his friends how to play cricket.

Leo thanked Mr Googly.

"I have really enjoyed playing cricket with you," he said.

"You have done very well, Leo," said Mr Googly. "Cricket is great fun but, like all sports, it takes a lot of practice to become a good player."

"I would love to be a good cricketer," said Leo.

"Well, next time I will teach you how to practise your cricket skills," said Mr Googly.

"I would like that," said Leo. "See you soon!"

Leo had learnt how to play another sport to help keep him fit and healthy.

He had bowled lots of balls and hit lots of shots, which was good exercise.

Remember, Leo says:

"Sport is fun! There are lots of different sports and activities to try and you can learn them all with me!"

Leo Learns Story Library

Titles available to buy online

Leo Learns Golf
Leo Learns Tennis
Leo Learns Football
Leo Learns Cricket

Many more titles COMING SOON! Including:

Leo Learns Rugby
Leo Learns Skiing
Leo Learns Snow Boarding
Leo Learns Athletics